12/25/67

TO BOBBY

WITH LOVE

AUNT LILLIAN & UNCLE WALT

STORMS

STORMS

Their Origins and Effects · Forecasting and Weather Lore

by PAUL E. LEHR

illustrations by HARRY MC NAUGHT
and NINO CARBE

 GOLDEN PRESS · NEW YORK

Library of Congress Catalog Card Number 62-9855

Picture on page 11 © 1956 by Golden Press, Inc. Pictures on pages 14, 15, 16, 18, 19, t. 21, 23, 24, b. 26, 29, 30, 35, 39, 40, b. 45, 47, 57, © 1957 by Golden Press, Inc.

CONTENTS

The hurricane is a very destructive kind of storm.

What is a Storm?

At every moment of the day and night, many kinds of storms are raging over land and sea. At this very moment 1,800 thunderstorms are spitting lightning, soaking the earth with tons of rain, and flattening crops with hail. Blizzards and other snow storms are whitening parts of the winter hemisphere of the earth. Waterspouts are whirling over the tropical oceans. Somewhere over a lonely ocean current, a hurricane with its awesome winds may be forming. In New York, people may be looking at a cloudless sky, but not more than a thousand miles away other people are sheltering themselves from a storm.

A storm is a disturbance of the atmosphere, and is made up of such ele-

Lightning strikes during a night thunderstorm over the town of Olpe, Kansas.

ments as strong winds, rain, snow, hail, or blowing snow or dust. During some storms, destructive winds and flooding cause great damage. During a blizzard, snowdrifts pile up and block roads. Ice storms snap telephone poles and power lines, and break branches off trees.

A tornado, the most violent of storms, may pass over a town in a few minutes, its violent winds uprooting trees, demolishing houses, and taking lives. Tornadoes have torn wool from grazing sheep and plucked feathers from chickens. Once a man was sucked through an open window and was left hanging over a branch in a nearby tree. Stalks of wheat were found driven into trees. A 700-pound refrigerator was found 3 miles from the wrecked house out of which it had been lifted. Awakening unharmed, a small boy discov-

11

A tornado sweeps over a smaller area than does the hurricane, but it is often swifter, more violent, and more destructive where it does strike.

ered that his bed had been whisked from beneath him by the wind. A heavy railway engine was lifted from its rails and set down on another track headed in the opposite direction.

With wind speeds frequently 200 miles an hour, and sometimes as strong as 450 miles an hour, the tornado contrasts with the hurricane in size, violence, and duration. A hurricane, a massive, slow-moving storm, may take hours or even days to pass a town. Often stretching 400 miles across, the hurricane is about 2,000 times wider than the average tornado. The large size and slow movement of a hurricane make prediction of its path possible, but the pinpoint size and short life of thunderstorms and tornadoes make prediction of the exact location of their occurrence and their likely paths extremely difficult, if not impossible.

12

Distinctive forms of clouds and precipitation, as well as high winds, are common to storms. Precipitation is the weatherman's name for rain, drizzle, snow, hail, sleet, and other forms of water falling from the sky.

Clouds are the first sign of a coming storm. The clouds of a hurricane, for example, move in stealthily, signaling the approach of the storm to those who know the ways of weather. First come the wispy, veil-like cirrus clouds, gradually spreading a haze of ice crystals across the sky high overhead. The wind freshens, and the clouds darken a little; then, small fluffy cumulus clouds speed across the sky below the high decks of darkening clouds. Rain spatters fitfully, the wind gradually rises, and the clouds thicken more. Then with a full-throated roar, the tremendous winds of the hurricane arrive.

A knowledge of the causes of wind, precipitation, and different kinds of clouds will help to make clear what a storm is and why it behaves as it does. Getting the facts about the ingredients of weather makes it easier to understand the descriptions of thunderstorms, tornadoes, and hurricanes that follow.

Tornadoes in the United States are most common in the South and Midwest. But the town of Greendale, Massachusetts, will remember this one, which struck on June 9, 1953.

Winds

Mountain breezes in daytime

Mountain breezes at night

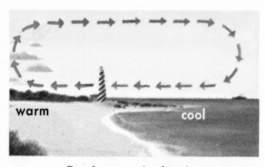

Sea breezes in daytime

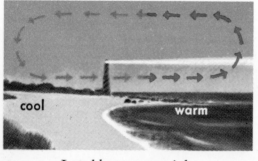

Land breezes at night

Wind is moving air. Air may stand still, so that there is a calm, but most of the time it is moving at least a few miles per hour.

Winds are caused by differences in atmospheric pressure. At the level of the ocean, the atmosphere presses down on the earth with an average force of 14.7 pounds on each square inch, or over a ton on every square foot. On land the pressure gets less as one moves to higher and higher altitudes. In some places the pressure is less, in other places more, and it is always changing. Just as water flows downhill, so air flows from areas where the pressure is high to areas where the pressure is low.

Differences in pressure are caused by unequal heating of the earth's surface by the sun. Where the earth is heated strongly, the air above it is warmed and becomes lighter. Hence the pressure decreases. Where there is no heat from the sun, as happens at night, the air cools and becomes heavier, so the pressure increases.

At the seashore, the sand absorbs heat from the sun, and warms the air above it. The sea, however, reflects most of the sunlight, so the air above the water is warmed only a little or not at all. As the warm, light air above the sand rises, the cooler, heavier air over the sea flows onshore. This wind is called a sea breeze and shows, on a

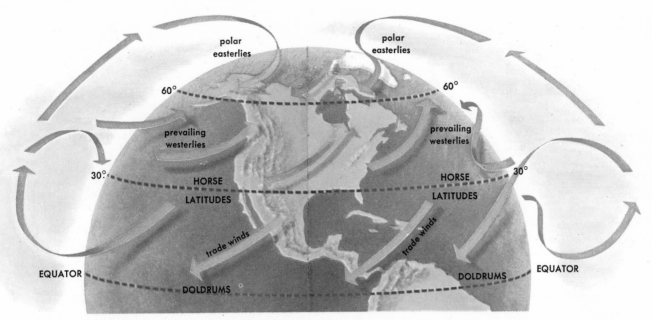

Wind directions in the northern hemisphere are mapped here. Air rises over equatorial region, moves northward, and sinks over polar region. Rotation of earth deflects southward-blowing winds toward west, and northward-blowing winds toward east.

small scale, the typical flow of air from high pressure (over the sea) to low pressure (over the sand).

The winds over the earth behave much like the sea breeze, blowing from high to low pressures. Regions near the equator receive more heat than the polar regions; hence a belt of low pressure forms near the equator and one of higher pressure near each of the poles.

Because the earth rotates eastward, winds blowing toward the equator are turned toward the west, while winds blowing toward the poles are turned toward the east. The rotation of the earth is also the cause of the belts of high and low pressure between the equator and the poles.

Most storms are found in low-pressure areas, or "lows." The winds blowing around a low turn counterclockwise in the northern hemisphere, while the winds of a high-pressure area (a "high") blow clockwise around it. Since most storms move from west to east, the very first sign of a storm in the northern hemisphere is a south wind. As the low-pressure area with the storm passes over, the wind shifts from south to west to north.

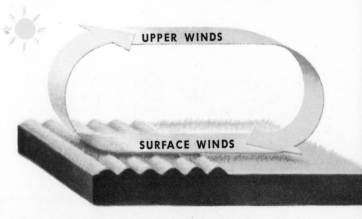

Unequal heating of the earth's surface may produce this circulation pattern.

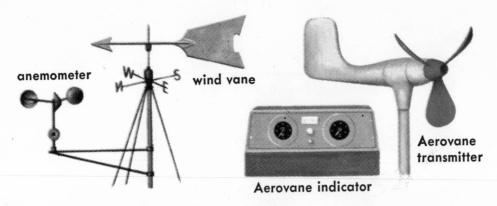

anemometer   wind vane

Aerovane transmitter

Aerovane indicator

The wind vane (or weather vane) indicates wind direction.
The other instruments here indicate wind speed.

Weather vanes, the oldest weather instruments known, show wind direction by pointing into the wind. An instrument called the anemometer has been developed to measure the speed of the wind. At airports and at weather stations, the revolving cups of the anemometer are seen just below the weather vane. When there is no wind the cups stand still. When the wind is strong the cups spin madly. The wind speed is recorded electrically.

In 1805, Admiral Beaufort of the British Navy invented a system of estimating wind speeds from their effect on the sails of a ship. He used numbers from 0 (a calm) to 12 (a wind of hurricane force). Admiral Beaufort's scale has been adopted for use on land also. In the table, Beaufort's number 3 is a gentle breeze (an 8- to 12-mile-an-hour wind) that keeps leaves and twigs in motion. Wind speeds are given both in miles per hour (mph) and knots, or nautical miles per hour. By international agreement, all wind speeds measured by meteorologists are reported in knots.

ESTIMATING WINDS ON THE BEAUFORT SCALE

Beaufort number	mph / knots	Description	Observation	Symbols on weather maps
0	0-1 / 0-1	calm	smoke rises vertically	calm
1	1-3 / 1-3	light air	smoke drifts slowly	calm
2	4-7 / 4-6	slight breeze	leaves rustle	5 knots
3	8-12 / 7-10	gentle breeze	leaves and twigs in motion	10 knots
4	13-18 / 11-16	moderate breeze	small branches move	15 knots
5	19-24 / 17-21	fresh breeze	small trees sway	20 knots
6	25-31 / 22-27	strong breeze	large branches sway	25 knots
7	32-38 / 28-33	moderate gale	whole trees in motion	30 knots
8	39-46 / 34-40	fresh gale	twigs break off trees	35 knots
9	47-54 / 41-47	strong gale	branches break	45 knots
10	55-63 / 48-55	whole gale	trees snap and are blown down	50 knots
11	64-72 / 56-63	storm	widespread damage	60 knots
12	73-82 / 64-71	hurricane	extreme damage	70 knots

16

Stratocumulus clouds cruise over Lake Placid, New York, on a summer day. The weather was cool and breezy.

Clouds

Some storms are accompanied by almost every kind of cloud, others have just one kind, and a few have no clouds at all. Clouds are signs of weather that is coming.

How do clouds form? They form from moisture in the atmosphere. Even the air of a cloudless sky contains some water in the form of water vapor, a gas. This gas is made up of particles so small that they are invisible. At a certain temperature, the air can hold only so much water in this invisible form. If the air is already holding as much as it can, and the temperature then gets colder, some of the water vapor will condense. That is, it will form clouds, which consist of billions of very small water droplets. If the temperature is below freezing, tiny ice particles may form.

All clouds, then, consist of large numbers of water or ice particles being carried along by currents of air. What happens to clouds is an important part of the story of storms.

Clouds can be divided into four families. First are the family of high clouds, including cirrus, cirrocumulus, and cirrostratus. These are clouds made of

17

Cirrus: 5 miles high or more; thin and wispy.

Cirrocumulus: 4 to 5 miles high— making "mackerel" sky.

Cirrostratus: 4 to 5 miles high—thin, gauzy sheets

Altostratus: 6500 feet or more high— dense whitish or gray sheets.

Altocumulus: 6500 or more high— roll-like patches or layers.

Stratus: 6500 ft. or lower. A thick, gray blanket above the ground.

Stratocumulus: 6500 ft. or lower—puffy gray masses in layers.

Nimbostratus: darker than stratus with snow or rain falling; near the ground.

ice crystals, and are usually found at altitudes of 20,000 feet or higher. Cirrus clouds are wispy and featherlike. Cirrocumulus clouds are thin and patchy and form a "mackerel sky"—so called because the clouds resemble the patterns on a mackerel's back. Cirrostratus clouds form thin sheets or layers. Quite often a halo is seen around the moon or sun when cirrostratus clouds cover the sky.

The middle cloud family has two members: altostratus and altocumulus. Altostratus form a sheet or layer of clouds made of droplets of water. Altocumulus clouds are often seen as rows of whitish or grayish clouds covering much of the sky. The middle clouds are seen at heights from 6,500 feet to 20,000 feet.

The low cloud family consists of stratus, stratocumulus, and nimbostratus. Stratus makes a low-lying, sheet-like cloud. Stratocumulus are usually seen as long rolls of clouds covering nearly the whole sky. Nimbostratus are dark, ragged clouds that usually have rain or snow falling from them.

Members of the fourth family are the tall, vertical clouds. These are the cumulus and cumulonimbus forms. Cumulus are the white, fluffy clouds that you see on a fine day. Where a thunderstorm is brewing you see cumulonimbus clouds. The top of a cumulonimbus will often reach 50,000 to 60,000 feet and can reach as high as 75,000.

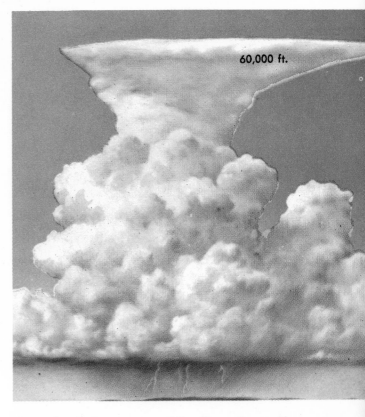

60,000 ft.

Cumulonimbus: up to 15 miles—the well-known thunderheads, with tops often blown into anvil shape.

Cumulus: formed (like cumulonimbus) by vertical air currents. They mean fair weather—unless they pile up into cumulonimbus.

19

Rain and snow often come at the wrong time.

Rain and Snow

Rain falls from clouds for the same reason anything else falls. The gravity of the earth pulls it down. Because water droplets or ice crystals in clouds are almost unbelievably tiny and light, the pull of gravity on each is very small. The average cloud droplet, only 1/2500 of an inch in diameter, would take 16 hours to fall half a mile in perfectly still air. But the atmosphere is always in motion and the motion under most clouds is upward. This works against the very slow downward pull of gravity, so the cloud droplets do not fall.

Although all clouds are made of water droplets or ice crystals, these do not always fall as rain or snow. Only when a cloud droplet grows to a diameter of at least 1/125 of an inch can it fall out of the cloud as rain. Since the average raindrop contains almost a million times as much water as a cloud droplet, tiny cloud droplets must increase tremendously in size to become large enough to fall out of the cloud as rain. The process by which cloud droplets grow is called "coalescence." This means "growing together into one body." Coalescence may occur in several ways.

Because the droplets in a cloud are of different sizes, they move at different speeds. When they hit each other, the large drops absorb the small ones, and finally become large enough to fall as rain.

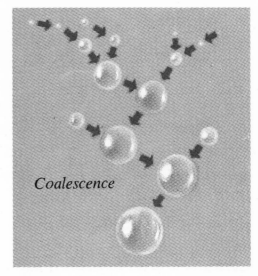

Coalescence

Another type of coalescence occurs when tiny ice crystals and water droplets are present in the same part of a cloud. Some of the water droplets evaporate; they become water vapor. The water vapor freezes onto the ice crystals. In this way the ice crystals grow until they become heavy enough to fall as snow or ice pellets. As these fall through the warm air closer to the earth, they melt and become raindrops.

Another cause of coalescence is electricity in clouds. Most clouds have either a positive or a negative charge of electricity. Thunderclouds have positive and negative charges in different parts of the same cloud. Air currents will sometimes mix these different parts of the cloud so that cloud droplets with different charges come next to each other. Drops with a positive charge are attracted by drops with a negative charge just like two magnets. When droplets with different charges come together they form a larger drop. These drops eventually grow large enough to fall as rain.

All snowflakes are six-sided, but no two flakes are exactly alike.

Snowflakes are crystals of ice. All snowflakes are six-sided, but no two are exactly alike. They are formed when water vapor crystallizes on a microscopic airborne bit of soil, rock, or volcanic ash. Snow crystals are the result. The cloud temperature must generally be between +10°F. and —4°F., however, before snow will start to form.

Sleet and freezing rain occur when rain, formed in warm air aloft, falls through a cold layer of freezing air. So-called "glaze" forms when very cold rain falls on cold surfaces and freezes instantly. A 1959 ice storm in central Illinois coated the countryside with tons of ice. Trees, telephone poles, and power lines crashed to the ground, leaving people without lights, telephones, or heat during the intensely cold weather, and driving was almost impossible.

Sleet consists of ice pellets. These are tiny beads of ice, usually not more than an eighth of an inch in diameter. They are sometimes clear but are more often cloudy white.

Hail is one of the hazards of a thunderstorm. Hailstones vary in size from about ¼ inch in diameter to more than five inches. The exact way in which hail grows to such a tremendous size is not known, but we do know that hail begins to form as frozen raindrops high up where the temperature is well below freezing. Although more is written in the newspapers about the great damage caused by tornadoes, hailstorms cause more losses, year in and year out, than tornadoes do. During 1951, the worst hailstorms on record hit the United States, and caused more than $75,000,-000 damage to property and crops.

The worst hailstorms in the United States occur in the Great Plains.

Glaze is sparkling and beautiful in the sun after a night of freezing rain, but power lines and trees suffer.

Fronts and Frontal Storms

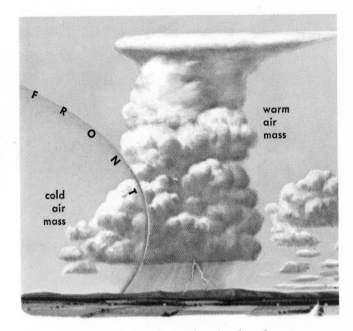

Cumulonimbus clouds with rain develop as a cold front moves in beneath warm air.

The weather reports in newspapers and on radio and television mention cold fronts and warm fronts, and "highs," "lows," and air masses. A high-pressure area, or "high," is a whirling mass of air which generally moves slowly from west to east. Between the highs are found the low-pressure areas, or "lows," into which the winds blow. In these lows are the unsettled weather and storms.

A *front* is formed when a high-pressure area of cold, heavy air (a cold air mass) overtakes another high containing lighter, warmer air (a warm air mass). These cold and warm air masses do not mix. The colder mass of air pushes under the warmer air and lifts it. Where this happens there is a weather front. As the warmer air is lifted along the front, the moisture in it condenses. This results in clouds, and often in rain, sleet, hail, or snow. Thus a front brings stormy weather.

As the colder mass of air advances, it forms a cold front. When a typical cold front moves into an area, there is first an increase of winds from the south or southwest; altocumulus clouds appear to the west or northwest, and the barometer begins to fall.

As the front draws closer, the clouds lower, and towering cumulonimbus clouds move in overhead. A spattering of rain starts, and becomes heavier as the wind increases and shifts to the west or north. Sometimes there are rain squalls and strong, gusty winds. With the front directly overhead, the barometer shows its lowest pressure. As the front moves away toward the east, the air clears rapidly; the barometer rises and the temperature drops. Winds become steady from the west or northwest.

If a cold front is moving fast, it may be preceded by a squall line. This is a line of black, threatening cumulonimbus clouds with tops rising to heights of 8 to 15 miles. The storms in these clouds may be incredibly violent and are avoided by all aircraft if possible. A light plane could be torn to pieces in a squall line. From the ground a squall line looks like an advancing wall of boiling black fog. Rain, whipped about by the wind, pours down in sheets. Flash

23

Sometimes a squall line, with dark clouds, violent gusts, and hard rain, moves in ahead of a cold front.

floods often result, and dry ravines or gullies may become filled with raging torrents.

When a warm mass of air advances, it forms a warm front. Warm fronts move about half as fast as cold fronts, and the rainy weather accompanying them usually lasts much longer but is less violent than cold-front weather. Warm fronts announce themselves as much as two days in advance. The first sign is the appearance of cirrus clouds high overhead. As the front approaches, they change to cirrostratus clouds. If cumulonimbus clouds appear, this means that the warm air is unstable. Unstable warm air rises faster than stable warm air, and so causes spotty rains and thunderstorms well ahead of the front line. If the warm air is stable, steady rain falls from a leaden sky overcast by altostratus and nimbostratus clouds. When the front passes, the rain stops, the sky clears, and the air turns warm. Warm-front weather is not considered stormy weather, unless there are thunderstorms. The steady rain of a warm front is the kind a farmer likes best.

A warm front moves in over a cold air mass, forming a typical series of clouds as it comes.

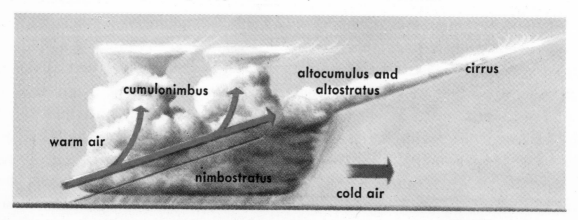

Thunderstorms

A thunderstorm is one of the most awesome sights of nature. Prehistoric man trembled at thunder and lightning. To him the sound and fury of the storm meant his gods were angry. The Norsemen said that the god Thor was hurling his hammer; American Indians thought the Thunderbird was in flight. Many primitive people today believe a thunderstorm is supernatural and look to their witch doctors for protection. Even the meteorologist today, with all his knowledge of the how and why of a thunderstorm, stands in awe of this tremendous outburst of power in the skies.

The base of a thunderstorm is usually in the warm, moist air close to the ground, while its top, which can tower as high as 75,000 feet, is up where the temperature is 60 to 70 degrees below zero Fahrenheit. The bottom of the cloud is made of liquid water droplets; the top consists of ice crystals. Within the cloud there are violent updrafts and downdrafts. These columns of rising and falling air can toss an airplane about and even wreck it. Downdrafts reaching the ground spread out to give us the cool, gusty wind that blows just before a thunderstorm arrives.

The thunderstorm itself is made up of several cumulonimbus cells. Each cell can be thought of as a smaller cloud that forms the larger cumulonimbus cloud. The development of each cell can be traced through three distinct stages. The *cumulus stage* is first. The diagram shows the rain and snow in this cell, the updrafts, the temperature at top and bottom, and the height—25,000 feet. Next is the *mature stage*. Here there are both updrafts and downdrafts; rain and sometimes hail are falling. The top, as shown, has reached 40,000 feet and has a temperature of −60°F. Then comes the final or *dissipating stage* of a thunderstorm cell; all air currents are mov-

Empire State Building, highest point in New York City area, is frequent target. Notice that lightning does not *zigzag.*

High in a thundercloud the electrical charge is positive; at bottom, negative.

base. The charge on the ground under a thunderstorm is positive. Since electricity flows from negative (−) to positive (+), a lightning stroke can go from the cloud to the ground or, within the cloud, from the base to the top. Lightning occurs when electrical pressure between parts of the cloud, or between cloud and ground, becomes high enough. Cloud-to-ground lightning starts with a thin "leader" stroke to the ground, followed almost instantly by a heavy return stroke from the ground. What we see as a single lightning flash is actually many back-and-forth flashes from cloud to ground, and ground to cloud, within a small fraction of a second. Fortunately, about 65% of all lightning strokes are within the cloud and never reach the ground at all.

ing downward, the rain has become light or has stopped, and high-level winds blow the ice crystals at the top of the cloud into the typical anvil shape.

Lightning is caused by the attraction of unlike electrical charges. A thunderstorm cloud has a positive charge near the top and a negative charge near the

DEVELOPMENT OF A THUNDERSTORM

(A) Rising air currents in cumulus clouds reach about 25,000 ft. (B) Moisture in air at high levels condenses, forming rain or ice crystals. These fall and chill lower air, causing downdrafts and winds near ground. (C) Air, now cooled, stops rising. Precipitation ceases. Wind blows top of thunderhead into anvil shape.

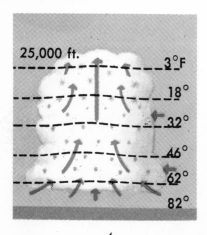

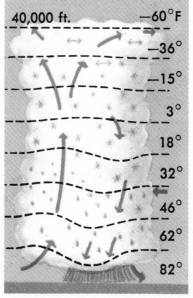

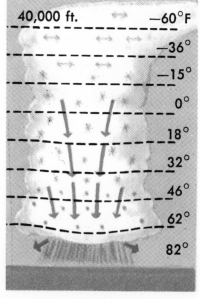

A

B

C

The power of a single lightning flash is tremendous. In the average home the available power is about 11,000 watts (110 volts x 100 amperes). A single lightning flash may discharge up to three trillion watts, but this happens in such a short time that there is no way to use this tremendous energy.

Lightning tends to hit the highest object on the ground under the storm. This object can be a church steeple, a house, a television antenna, a tree, or even a man standing in an open field. When a storm is overhead, objects that jut above the ground surface give off a concentrated stream of positive charges (point discharge), which attract the negative charges at the base of a cloud. The lightning is attracted to the point nearest to it. Benjamin Franklin studied point discharge and saw that high rooftops, trees, and steeples were nearly always the targets of lightning. So, he reasoned, if he could "catch" the lightning before it hit the roof he could lead it to the ground without harm to the building. He did this by erecting a pointed rod with its top four or five feet higher than the roof and its bottom end well grounded in damp earth. The first lightning rod invented by Franklin was installed in Philadelphia in 1753.

Thunder is caused by lightning. A flash of lightning heats the air in its path to about 15,000 degrees Centigrade (27,000°F.) in a millionth of a second or less. This heating causes the air to expand. Expanding air rushing outward

Lightning is attracted to the highest objects on the ground under the storm. For safety, avoid such high objects.

in all directions causes the sound we call thunder.

You can estimate your distance from a lightning flash because light and sound travel at different speeds. Light travels 186,000 miles a second, while sound travels only about 1,100 feet a second. Thus, you can see the lightning instantly,

HOW FAR AWAY IS THE LIGHTNING?

Time, in seconds, between seeing the flash and hearing the thunder	The lightning is actually this many miles away from you
5	1
10	2
15	3
20	4
25	5
30	6

27

LIGHTNING WRECKS SCHOOL
$100,000 Damage

It is well known that lightning often starts fires, but not so well known that it can cause blasts. Heat from the lightning bolt causes violent expansion of air, and this causes destruction.

School was not in session when lightning hit this building near Danville, Illinois. The charge apparently followed steel girders through the building, wrecking six rooms and causing one small fire. Inset shows one of wrecked rooms.

but the sound of the thunder travels toward you at the rate of one mile every 5 seconds. Count the number of seconds between the flash and the sound of thunder. Divide the number of seconds by 5 and you will have the distance in miles between you and the flash. You can estimate seconds by counting slowly.

When you hear thunder, remember the flash of lightning that caused the thunder you just heard cannot harm you.

However, it can warn you not to expose yourself needlessly to the next lightning strokes. Following are lists of DOs and DON'Ts for your protection against lightning.

Thunderstorms, despite the hail, lightning, and wind damage they cause, do more good than harm. The principal benefit is the rain they bring. A second benefit that few people realize is that thunderstorms help keep the soil fertile.

28

DOs	DON'Ts
Stay in your car.	*Don't stay out on a high, exposed place.*
Go indoors if possible.	*Don't stand under a lone tree.*
Get under a cliff or ledge.	*Don't stand up or work in an open field.*
Lie flat, if necessary, in an open field or ditch.	*Don't stay near a wire fence.*
Ground your television antenna.	*Don't go swimming.*
Stay out of boats and away from the water.	*Don't repair your TV antenna during a storm.*

Millions of tons of nitrous oxide, a good fertilizer, are formed by lightning as it causes nitrogen and oxygen in the air to unite. These nitrous oxides dissolve in rain and fall to the ground to help enrich the soil.

The total energy of a single thunderstorm is equivalent to that of hundreds of atomic bombs. However, control of such tremendous forces by man is not possible today, nor will it be in the foreseeable future.

During a thunderstorm, an auto is a safe refuge. An airplane also is usually safe in lightning. A television antenna that is not grounded is dangerous.

Tornadoes

A tornado is a thunderstorm gone mad. A thunderstorm will sometimes develop a small, very intense whirlpool near its center. This whirlpool becomes a twisting, whirling funnel cloud hanging from the bottom of the thunderstorm —a tornado.

Tornadoes are the most violent and destructive storms. A hurricane may be 2,000 times as large as the average tornado, but is less than half as violent. Tornadoes are so violent that houses in their path may fly apart like matchsticks. Automobiles, large animals, and even locomotives have been lifted and hurled aside.

Tornadoes, fortunately, have a small diameter. Their paths of destruction are rarely more than a quarter of a mile wide and average only 10 to 12 miles in length, but the destruction within the tornado path is almost total. Buildings are reduced to rubble, large trees are snapped like toothpicks, smaller objects are picked up and smashed, or carried for miles. The funnel cloud may drop down to the ground, travel a short distance, lift up for a while and then drop to the ground again. The winds may reach 300 to 400 miles an hour but probably average about 200 miles an hour. Updrafts in tornadoes have been estimated to reach the same speed. These wind speeds cannot be measured but are estimated from the damage they cause.

Torrential rains, intense lightning, and often hail go along with the strong

Mammatocumulus clouds may be a sign that a tornado will soon develop.

When the ominous funnel appears, the best place to be is in a storm shelter.

The destructive power of a tornado is due partly to the force of the 200- to 400-mile-an-hour whirling winds, and partly to the very low atmospheric pressure within the funnel.

winds of a tornado. Extremely low pressure is found in funnel clouds. The pressure of air trapped inside a closed house or barn will cause it to explode outward as the partial vacuum of the funnel passes close by. Tornado winds can have a force 900 times that of a 10-mile-an-hour breeze. The large hailstones of a tornado can also cause damage. On June 5, 1917, disk-shaped hailstones 6 to 10 inches in diameter and 2 to 3 inches thick fell near Topeka, Kansas. Hail of this size is capable of tearing holes in a roof, injuring a man seriously, and destroying crops and livestock. The lightning of a tornado is extremely brilliant, much brighter and bluer than in any other kind of storm. At night, or when the bottom of the thundercloud is hidden from sight, these intense flashes can serve as a warning of an impending tornado.

The damage caused by tornadoes is fantastic. Accounts of damage and the freak effects of tornado winds seem more like horror fiction than fact. A Kansas twister on June 5, 1917, flattened 35 miles of wheat fields, demolishing every house in its path. A lighted kerosene lamp was blown several hundred yards and found still burning and undamaged. A herd of steers was seen floating through the air like "gigantic birds."

Tornadoes have lifted frogs and fish from ponds, and dropped them over

31

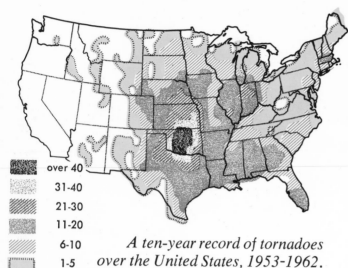

over 40
31-40
21-30
11-20
6-10
1-5

A ten-year record of tornadoes over the United States, 1953-1962.

populated areas. Red clay lifted into the air by the twister and mixed with rain falls to the ground again some distance away, giving rise to stories of "a rain of blood."

The violent thunderstorms in which tornadoes occur are found most often in squall lines that form in the warm air ahead of cold fronts. Tornadoes usually move from southwest to northeast but have been known to skip, make U-turns, even make a perfect circle. The average forward speed of a tornado is 45 miles an hour. Individual tornadoes, however, have remained stationary for a few minutes, others have drifted as slowly as five miles an hour, and in a few cases a forward speed of 65 miles an hour has been recorded.

Tornadoes occur in many parts of the world. England, Europe, Asia, Africa, and Australia have all reported tornadoes, but the United States has a greater number than the rest of the world together. In the United States, the Central Plains are struck most frequently.

Tornadoes also occur over water, where they produce waterspouts. They have very much the same appearance as land tornadoes except for the whirling spray of water seen where the funnel touches the ocean. Waterspouts are quite numerous over the tropical oceans when cloud conditions are favorable; as many as ten at a time can be seen from an airplane flying over tropical waters. While tornadoes are always accompanied by thunderstorms, waterspouts are seen most often with well-developed cumulus clouds that have not yet become thunderstorms. Only once in a very great while does a waterspout move in over land. One did move onshore in the Bahama Islands in 1959, where it did quite a bit of damage to boats, docks, and beach houses, but this waterspout died out as it moved inland. Waterspouts and hurricanes apparently have this in common: both lose strength on moving inland.

Tornadoes and violent thunderstorms are most frequent during the months of May and June. Conditions then are just right over "Tornado Alley," a wide belt through the middle of the continent from the Gulf of Mexico to Minnesota and Wisconsin. Warm, moist air moving north over the broad Mississippi River valley from the Gulf of Mexico clashes with cold air coming from the northwest. The unstable warm air is lifted violently, and heavy thunderstorms are formed. If the warm air is unusually unstable and the cold air gives it enough of a lift, the thunderstorms formed develop tornado funnels. Four or five o'clock in the afternoon, the warmest part of the day, is a favored time for tornadoes.

At the start of the tornado season in March, northern Mississippi is hardest hit. April finds the area of maximum tornadoes spreading to Missouri, Texas, Oklahoma, and Kansas. During May and June, "Tornado Alley" extends in a broad belt from Oklahoma to southern Minnesota and Wisconsin. July, August, and September are months of less activity over the same area. Sixty-eight per cent of all tornadoes occur during April, May, and June; 21 per cent occur from July through October; and only 11 per cent the rest of the year.

If you live anywhere east of the Rockies you stand some chance of witnessing a tornado but not much chance of being hurt by one. In an average year, about 35,000 people in the United States are killed in traffic accidents. This is over twice as many as the total killed by tornadoes in the past 50 years.

Tornadoes have been reported every hour of the day and night every month of the year. Because of this constant possibility, the United States Weather

A waterspout appears offshore at Solana Beach, California. Several hours earlier, a tornado hit the nearby town of Oceanside.

Bureau and other weather services keep a year-round watch to forecast and warn people of tornado danger.

Tornado forecasting is one of the most difficult tasks for the weather scientist. In the 1880's, during the early days of weather forecasting, the United States Army Signal Corps issued tornado warnings, but soon discontinued these because the forecasts were little better than guesswork.

Today, a great network of surface and upper-air observation stations has made it possible to tell which are the areas where tornadoes are likely to strike. But it is still impossible to pinpoint just when and where.

A continuous tornado watch is kept at the Severe Weather Center in Kansas City. This center devotes all its efforts toward detecting and forecasting weather likely to produce tornadoes and severe thunderstorms. When such a situation develops, a warning is issued. Radio and television stations alert local residents.

People who live in areas where tornadoes strike should know how to protect themselves. The "cyclone cellar" is one of the safest places to be during a tornado. Many farms in the Middle West states have them. The Red Cross recommends concrete shelters 6 feet wide, 8 feet long, 7 feet deep. A shelter of this size can hold at least eight people. The door should face northeast, since most tornadoes travel from the southwest. The door must be made of heavy timber and have a strong bar inside to keep it from flying open when the tornado passes overhead. A storm shelter is good insurance. No one has ever been killed in one.

If there is no storm shelter, the southwest corner of the basement of a frame house is the safest place.

In a house with no basement, one should go to the southwest corner of the ground floor, away from windows, and get under a mattress or bed. Do not remain standing, especially near a window. Even small objects blown by a 200-mile-an-hour wind can kill. In the business district of a city, a building of concrete with a steel frame is the safest place to be during a tornado. Flatten yourself against an inside wall on the ground floor. Stay away from the windows. Out of doors, if a tornado is close and coming in your direction, lie down in any depression in the ground. Do not remain standing—even a gutter or curbing can offer some protection.

"Cyclone cellar"

Hurricanes

"Hurricane" is the West Indian name for the great tropical cyclones best known in the Caribbean. They are circular storms averaging 400 miles across. The winds of a hurricane blow at least 75 miles an hour, and often reach 125 miles an hour. The highest wind speed ever recorded for a hurricane was 186 miles an hour (at higher speed the wind gauges blew away), and speeds of over 200 miles per hour have been estimated.

Like all cyclones, tropical cyclones are low-pressure areas. Low-pressure areas in temperate regions north and south of the tropics have both cold and warm air within them. But the tropical cyclone (usually over the ocean) contains only warm, moist air. While a low-pressure area in temperate zones can sometimes be followed right around the world as it moves, the tropical cyclone, or hurricane, usually breaks up as soon as it moves inland.

In this book all tropical cyclones will be called hurricanes. However, keep in mind that these storms are known by many names in various parts of the world. In the western Pacific they are called "typhoons"; in Australia, "willy-willies"; in the Philippines, "baguios";

The eye of Hurricane Gloria was safely photographed from an airplane.

Hurricane Debbie, in 1961, was photographed from the Mercury Spacecraft, which traveled at a maximum altitude of 158.6 miles.

and in the Indian Ocean hurricanes are known as "cyclones." The South Atlantic is the only ocean where hurricanes are unknown.

A hurricane is a giant "doughnut" of clouds, fearsome winds, and heavy rain, with occasional tornadoes thrown in for good measure. It has a center called an "eye." The eye is a clear or lightly clouded, nearly windless circular area usually about 15 miles in diameter, surrounded by a wall of clouds which marks the band of the strongest winds of the hurricane. The sudden drop in wind and the appearance of a sunny sky as the eye passes often fool people into thinking the storm is over. Then, as the other side of the hurricane moves in, the storm returns in its full fury. Weather maps, photographs, radar images, and flights into hurricanes have all confirmed this picture. A photograph of the picture on a radarscope shows that the storm has an "eye" surrounded by spiral bands of rain. A picture taken from an airplane flown high over a typhoon shows an almost perfect circular "eye." The eye is sometimes oval or not completely surrounded by clouds. Some hurricanes have two eyes.

A diagram of a hurricane (see next page) as seen from above divides it into quarters. The front half and the north side of a hurricane usually have the strongest winds. Thus, in a hurricane moving east to west, the right front quarter will have the strongest winds. Obviously it's better to have a hurricane pass north of you than south of you.

Trace the diagram on transparent paper and move it over a coastal town on a map. Notice how wind speeds and directions change as the hurricane passes over.

Strong winds and storm tides, over three times normal height, are the destructive forces of a hurricane. The 75- to 100-mile-an-hour winds extend outward from the wall of the eye, cutting a swath of destruction 25 to 500 miles

In 1958, a U.S. Navy Hurricane Reconnaissance aircraft studied Hurricane Daisy by means of radar. Airplane was at bright spot in center of photo, about 45 miles from the eye. Bright areas show where rain was heavy.

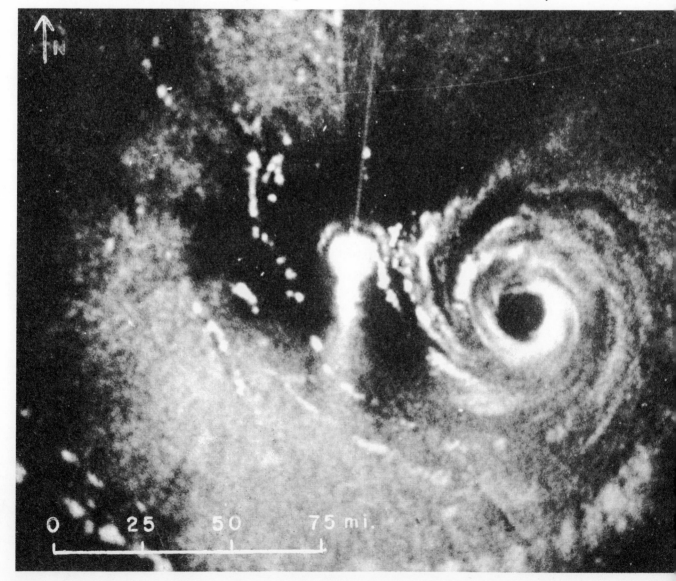

A HURRICANE WIND DIAGRAM

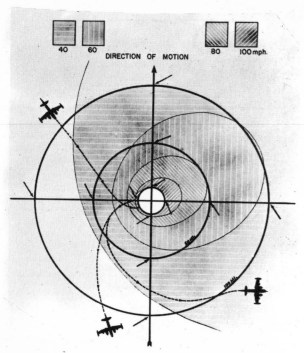

DIRECTION OF MOTION

40   60   80   100 mph.

wide. Trees are uprooted, and buildings leveled. The rain seems to blow horizontally, large pieces of debris are carried along, and the unearthly howl of the wind seems to fill the air.

The storm tides and waves of a hurricane cause floods. The storm waves are like very high tides, 10 to 15 feet higher than normal. Sometimes a storm wave arrives suddenly, flooding the coast with-

out warning. Such a wave hit Cuba at Santa Cruz del Sur on November 9, 1932. Twenty-five hundred people lost their lives as the storm wave carried the village away. Winds in this storm were estimated at 210 miles an hour but the storm wave was the main cause of the destruction. Similar waves have been reported wherever hurricanes hit. At the mouth of the Hooghly River, on the Bay of Bengal, 300,000 people were swept away by a storm tide in 1737. In 1864, a storm tide at the same place took another 50,000 lives.

Tremendous amounts of rain fall as a hurricane passes: 23 inches of rain fell in 24 hours at Taylor, Texas, in a 1921 hurricane. At Baguio in the Philippines, a world record rainfall was measured in July 1911. Forty-six inches of rain fell in 24 hours. The total four-day rain for this storm was 88 inches. If this rain had accumulated, the whole town would have been in water 7 feet 4 inches deep. (One inch of rain over one square mile amounts to 17.4 million gallons of water.)

DEVELOPMENT OF A HURRICANE

(A) opposing winds in tropical zone start moist air whirling. (B) Moisture in rising air condenses, releasing much heat. (C) Heat causes whirling air to rise faster and faster. (D) Air rushes in violently at bottom to replace rising air.

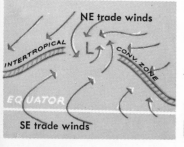

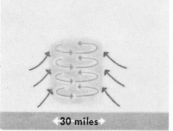

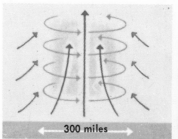

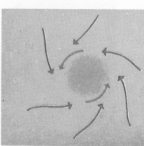

A   B   C   D

The tremendous force of hurricane winds builds tides higher. Ocean waters may sweep miles inland.

Hurricanes are given names for identification. Each year an alphabetical listing is assigned. The first might be "Alice," the second "Betsy," the third "Carol," and so on.

In 1955, Hurricane Connie crossed the North Carolina coast and curved across the Middle Atlantic states, dropping heavy rain over a large area. Close on Connie's heels, Hurricane Diane moved in, loosing torrential rains over the area just soaked by Connie. The disastrous floods that followed took 179 lives and destroyed a billion dollars in property.

A tropical cyclone can be traced through its stages of development. The map on the next page shows a storm starting west of the Cape Verde Islands. At this stage, the winds are less than 32 miles an hour, so the future hurricane, which we shall call "Carol," is classified as just a tropical low (L).

As the cyclone moves west, we find Carol has become a tropical storm with wind speeds between 32 and 73 miles an hour. As Carol continues moving westward at 10 to 12 miles an hour, the winds increase to hurricane force—over 74 miles an hour. Carol, now mature, crashes into Guadeloupe. Still moving westward at 10 to 12 miles an hour, Carol passes south of Puerto Rico and Haiti, with winds slowly increasing. Next Carol begins to curve north and passes over Cuba and the Bahamas, bludgeoning the islands with 125-mile-an-hour winds. Carol then turns, or recurves, to the northeast, speeding up to 30 miles an hour as the wind speed drops rapidly to less than 75 miles an hour. Somewhere north of Bermuda, Carol hits a cold front and eventually ends up as a storm in the North Sea.

The path taken by Hurricane Carol is typical of hurricane paths. However, hurricanes can be depended upon to do the unexpected. In 1955 Betsy followed an "ideal" path. Greta was more than somewhat fickle.

The hurricane season of the Atlantic reaches maximum intensity during August, September, and October. Over 84% of all hurricanes occur in these summer and early fall months. June, July, and November account for 14%, and less than 2% occur during the remaining six months of the year.

For the past 30 years there has been an average of five hurricanes per year in the Caribbean. The greatest number in any one year was eleven in 1950.

In the western North Pacific the active typhoon season lasts from July through November. The Pacific usually has more than 20 typhoons every year.

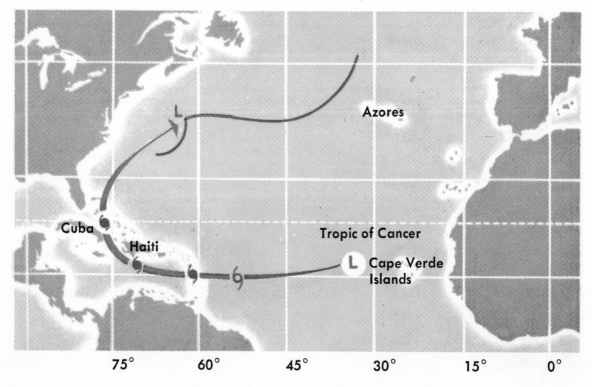

Hurricane Carol, typical of many, started in the eastern Atlantic, moved westward, reached the West Indies, then turned northeast.

Hurricane winds drive sea water against a parkway in Brooklyn, New York. The impact of the water breaks up masonry, and strong currents scatter the debris.

Signs of the Hurricane

One of the first signs of an approaching hurricane is the storm swell on the ocean. Waves blown up by the hurricane travel for hundreds of miles, to break heavily upon a distant shore. As the hurricane, still far out at sea, approaches, the tides start to rise. A banded veil of cirrus clouds gradually advances to cover the sky. Finally, an arc of dense clouds appears on the horizon. This is the hurricane itself.

As the storm moves in from the sea, low, ragged clouds moved quickly by the wind—"scud clouds"—appear. An observer on the shore facing the storm sees these clouds move with the wind from his left to his right. The winds are light at first, then gradually increase in strength. The barometer starts to fall, rain blown by gusty winds spatters briefly, then the storm begins. Squalls lashed by violent winds follow each other in rapid succession. The rain comes in sheets, and over all is the deep-throated roar of the hurricane.

A hurricane warning system was established in 1938 by the United States Weather Bureau. Before this warning system was established, 161 lives were lost for every 10 million dollars' worth of property destroyed. In the period 1941-1945, this ratio was reduced to 4 lives lost for each 10 million dollars' worth of property damage. During the

Hurricane winds hurled this stick of wood like a spear through the palm tree.

scopes and weather equipment, fly into the storm once every six hours. Reports sent back by the planes tell the exact location of the storm center, the size of the eye, the speed of the winds, and the direction of the storm's movement.

The idea of sending airplanes out to track hurricanes was first discussed seriously in 1937, but was discarded as too dangerous. On July 27, 1943, when a hurricane was approaching his home town of Galveston, Texas, Colonel Joseph B. Duckworth, an instructor at the instrument flying school at Bryan, Texas, decided to take a look at the storm. With his navigator, Lt. Ralph O'Hair, he took off in a single-engine two-seater airplane, flew into the eye of the storm, and returned to the air-

August 1949 hurricane in Florida, only 2 lives were lost, while $52,000,000 damage was estimated.

In 1957 Hurricane Audrey hit the Louisiana coast. Despite a warning 48 hours in advance and urgent warnings repeated 14 hours in advance, people at Cameron, Louisiana, refused to leave. More than 500 people lost their lives when Audrey brought in a storm tide of over 10 feet and winds estimated at 150 miles per hour.

Reconnaissance aircraft, constantly searching the breeding grounds of tropical storms, spot a developing storm days before it comes near any land, and follow its movement continuously. These aircraft, equipped with radar-

base. In the meantime, a weather officer at the base heard of the flight, and when the plane landed begged the pilot to take him up for a look. So the first flight into the eye of a hurricane was followed almost immediately by a second flight. At 5:43 p.m. CST they flew into the eye, and by seven o'clock were back on the ground with the first meteorological account of a deliberate flight into a hurricane.

This eyewitness account provided proof that most of the dangers of flights into hurricanes were overrated. At the time this flight was made, it was thought that the turbulent winds in a hurricane would tear the wings off any airplane unlucky enough to wander into the storm. It was also thought that should a plane be lucky enough to reach the center of the storm undamaged, the downdrafts in the eye would surely force it down to the ocean, where escape from the boiling seas would be impossible. On this flight the turbulence at the level where the plane flew through the storm was no worse than that met outside hurricanes, and in fact was seldom as heavy. The downdraft in the eye, furthermore, was not strong enough to affect the flight.

In spite of the ease with which Colonel Duckworth penetrated the Galveston hurricane, a flight into a hurricane is not like taking a Sunday afternoon drive into the country. But after the first flights, more airplanes were sent into the big storms to observe. Penetrations were tried at high levels and low levels, and much was discovered about the kinds of weather to be expected in various parts of the storm. Low-level flights were made at 300 to 700 feet above the sea surface. Flying at this low level is very tricky; below 300 feet turbulence is heavy to violent; above 700 feet there will usually be clouds, which interfere with observations. The pilot, therefore, has to fly at a closely calculated height. As the flight proceeds from the edge of the storm, the pilot flies with the wind. The pressure begins

The swells which make breakers are produced by winds blowing over vast ocean areas. Hurricane winds build up these swells, which are one of the first signs of an approaching hurricane.

43

to drop, the winds increase, the sea begins to look rougher and rougher.

As a spiral arm is penetrated, there is a heavy downpour of rain for a few minutes. An almost clear area comes next—just before the main edge of the storm appears as a solid black wall. From the wall to the edge of the eye, a distance sometimes as much as 200 miles, the clouds are solid overhead, a driving rain penetrates every chink and crevice, and the sea is a froth of wind-whipped waves.

When the wind hits 60 miles an hour, the pilot heads for the center with the wind on his left rear quadrant. Turbulence has been light but now gets heavier and heavier, until suddenly the plane breaks out into the eye of the storm. The wind in the eye dies down to a breeze, the sun is shining, and the sea below seems to boil. The crew looks out on the layers of clouds that form

Observers in a Hurricane Reconnaissance aircraft study the eye of a hurricane.

a high circular wall from the sea to as high as the eye can see. After a moment to relax and drink coffee, the crew goes back to work. Instruments are read, the meteorologist codes his observation, the navigator checks position, and the radio man begins sending back weather information, with the position and speed of the storm. Then the return trip begins. Seat belts are buckled, everything is fastened down, and the pilot heads for the wall of the eye.

After a brief encounter with heavy turbulence, the flight proceeds out from the storm center. Turbulence decreases steadily, the driving rain gradually falls off, the winds decrease, and the pilot sets his course for the airfield. Throughout the flight a steady stream of weather information has been radioed back to the forecasters. When the weather plane lands, the flight meteorologist and the crew brief the airfield weather staff on the whole flight.

High-level penetrations are quite different. Flights are made either at the 500-millibar pressure level (approximately 18,500 feet) or at 700 millibars (about 9,800 feet). At 500 millibars turbulence is much lighter than at any other level, but icing can become a great hazard, forcing the plane to seek lower levels. At 700 millibars the plane flies in clouds a great deal of the time, and encounters more steady turbulence, with occasional unexpected spots of heavy turbulence. At the high levels, the crew uses radar to "see" the storm, and as the

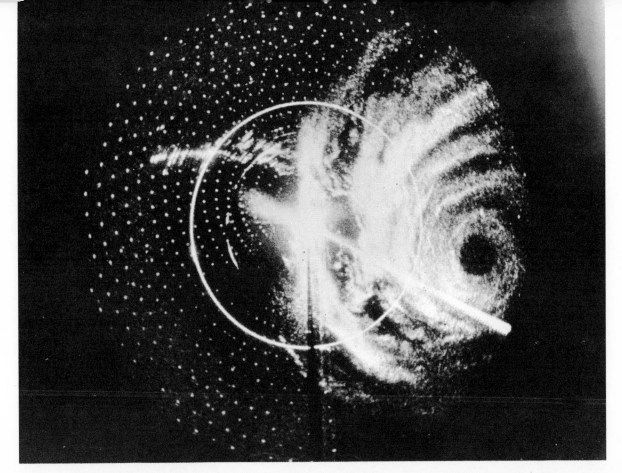

This photograph of Hurricane Gracie was taken by Navy radar over Florida. Storm was starting to break up. Dots on screen are due to interference.

plane flies toward the storm center, dropsondes (special measuring instruments) are thrown out of chutes to measure conditions of temperature, pressure, and humidity in the storm. A dropsonde measures the same things as a radiosonde. Unlike a radiosonde, which is carried aloft by a hydrogen-filled balloon, a dropsonde falls and radios information back to the airplane as it drifts down on its parachute to the sea.

By 1945, the military services had trained pilots to conduct regular reconnaissance flights to probe these fearsome tropical storms. The Air Force and Navy have divided the Atlantic into "areas of responsibility" where each keeps constant watch to discover and track tropical storms. In the Pacific the Air Force does this job alone. Despite the rough flying in the hurricane and the thousands of flights made, only three aircraft have been lost since the

The radar antenna sends out signals which are reflected by the hurricane, received by the antenna, and shown as a pattern on the observer's radar screen.

flight program was started in 1943.

Meteorological satellites can now take television pictures of hurricanes from hundreds of miles above the earth. This means that reconnaissance planes will not have to search for a storm. When the satellite picture shows that a storm is brewing, the planes can fly directly to it to measure its speed, winds, pressure, and so on.

Every possible type of equipment is used to detect and watch hurricanes. Airborne and land-based radar watches the storm at close range; automatic weather stations on uninhabited islands send back wind and pressure reports; upper-air sounding reports tell the forecaster what is going on in the high atmosphere ahead of the hurricane.

Even earthquake experts are on the lookout for hurricanes. Their seismographs, or "earthquake detectors," record shock waves traveling through the earth. They can also record microseisms, or very light shock waves, from ocean areas where there are hurricanes.

The Tiros satellites started a new age in weather observing. A weather satellite while orbiting the earth continually takes pictures showing the development and movements of storms and other weather systems.

A Tiros photograph can show an entire hurricane. This is Hurricane Anna, 1961.

The age-old cry "Why don't we do something about it?" is raised whenever a hurricane strikes. Something has been done. The hurricane warning system has certainly reduced loss of life. People have suggested that something be done to break up a hurricane before it can do any damage. Perhaps this will be possible 50 or 100 years from now, but our present knowledge shows us no way to "kill" or "steer" a hurricane away from land.

Dr. Irving Langmuir and Dr. Bernard Vonnegut, two scientists who worked for General Electric Corporation, experimented with cloud seeding after World War II. With another GE scientist, Dr. Vincent Schaefer, they found that they could "seed" clouds with dry ice to induce rain to fall, or, using a different seeding technique, cause clouds to break up. This brought the suggestion that a hurricane could be broken up by seeding it with dry ice. Unfortunately, the conditions in a hurricane are such that seeding might increase the intensity of the storm rather than decrease it.

Others suggested blowing the storm to bits with atomic or hydrogen bombs. But the energy needed to "run" a hurricane for one minute is equal to the energy of 1,000 atom bombs, so it would be impossible to A-bomb a hurricane into oblivion. Also, atom-bombing a hurricane would make it radioactive, and this would create a great hazard if the storm moved inland over populated areas.

Scientific research which may enable us to better understand, and perhaps some day to control, hurricanes is being carried on by the United States Weather Bureau at the National Hurricane Research Center in Florida and at various universities.

Dry ice dropped from an airplane into stratus clouds causes some to drop their moisture, leaving open pathways.

Strong Winds and Bad Weather

Besides thunderstorms, tornadoes, and hurricanes, there are many kinds of storms and bad weather in different parts of the world. Some of these are so interesting that they are famous everywhere. Certain winds cause such well-marked changes in weather that they are called by specific, local names where they occur.

One of these is the *foehn* wind, a hot, dry wind that flows down mountain slopes in many different parts of the world. The foehn was originally believed to blow only in certain valleys

Strong winds often accompany snowstorms.

of the Swiss Alps, but when the reason the foehn acts as it does was discovered, many other winds with different names were found to be foehns.

As the foehn wind blows down a mountainside, it warms 5½°F. for every thousands feet of descent. In North America, the foehn is called a *chinook*. This wind is forced down the eastern slopes of the Rocky Mountains by strong winds aloft. A foehn wind, be it in Austria, Switzerland, or North America, often causes temperatures to rise as much as 30°F. in 15 or 20 minutes. Snow and ice literally disappear in a few hours, either melting or evaporating directly into the dry, hot air. Because of this the foehn is sometimes called the "snow eater," in America, and *Schneefresser,* which is German for "snow eater," in Europe. The foehn is so very dry that it makes the wooden walls and floors of houses dry and split. Furniture comes unglued and everything is brittle with dryness. In Alpine villages, where most houses are constructed of wood, this dryness becomes a fire hazard. Foehn watchers, or fire watchers, go from house to house to see that all fires are put out and no one smokes. In the Rocky Mountain states, the chinook creates similar hazards but since the wind does not last so long, the fire watch is not so necessary.

The *zonda* of Argentina and southern Chile is also a foehn wind which blows down the slopes of the Andes Mountains. Foehn winds are called the *bohorok* in Sumatra, the *warm braw* in the Schouten Islands, off the north coast of New Guinea, and the *double foehn* on the west coast of Greenland. The *berg* wind of South Africa and the *sirocco*, called a *Ghibli* as it blows down the north slopes of the Atlas Mountains, are also foehn winds. When the sirocco crosses the Mediterranean Sea to Sicily and Italy, it picks up much moisture from the sea surface. As it passes over the mountains of Sicily, the sirocco is again compressed and warmed to bring additional scorching heat to Palermo, on the north side of the island, drying vegetation and ruining growing crops as it goes. The list of foehn winds, with all its local names, would cover pages. Foehns in France are known as *autans* and *marins*, in California as *northers* and *Santa Anas,* in New Zealand as *northwesters,* and so on and on. Wherever there are mountains, a foehn wind can blow.

Another type of mountain wind is the *fall wind*. All fall winds have the same general cause. Surface air cooled by contact with snow or with the cold ground flows downhill from plateaus or mountains into warmer valleys below. Fall winds are so cold that compression does not warm them sufficiently to bring temperatures up to normal by the time the winds reach level land or the sea. The *bora* is the cold fall wind that blows down to the Adriatic Sea. The *mistral* of southern France, which speeds down the Rhone Valley, sometimes reaching 60 miles an hour or more, is a combination of a fall wind and a down-valley wind. The same sort of wind is called the *maestral* where it sweeps into the Gulf of Genoa.

A whole group of cold winds, which have various meteorological causes, are classified as *northers*. The norther of Texas and Oklahoma is a fast-moving mass of cold air that follows a cold front moving southward along the east side of the Rocky Mountains. A norther in Texas brings strong north winds, and sudden drops in temperature of 20 to 35 degrees Fahrenheit in as little as two hours. Sometimes the norther sweeps southward along the east coast of Mexico to the Gulf of Campeche and the Yucatan Peninsula. If it is strong enough the cold air piles up in the Gulf of Campeche until it spills over Chivela Pass into the Gulf of Tehuantepec on the Pacific Ocean side. Here, where it is called the *Tehuantepecer*, wind speeds range from 40 to 70 miles an hour. A Tehuantepecer usually lasts only a few hours, but occasionally blows for several days. Sometimes this norther, which started out as a Texas norther, reaches Honduras and Nicaragua. In these countries it is called a *norte*, and in Costa Rica it goes by the peculiar name *papagayo*.

Another norther, an annoying and warm one, is the *bad-i-sad-o-bistroz*, or "wind of 120 days," which blows from the northwest in the Seistan district of Afghanistan and northeastern Iran. This wind, also known as the Seistan, blows almost incessantly during May through the end of August. Reaching speeds up to 70 miles an hour, it carries sand and gravel, forms and moves sand dunes, and brings general discomfort throughout its path.

Like the *bad-i-sad-o-bistroz*, many winds carry sand, dust, gravel, or snow. The snow-carrying winds are the *blizzards*. A true blizzard is marked by intense cold, strong winds, and powdery dry snow that is piled by the wind into drifts. Blizzards occur in the interior of continents over such areas as the northern plains of the United States, the central provinces of Canada, and the Arctic and Antarctic. On the steppes and plains of Russia a blizzard is called the *buran*.

Blizzards in North America sometimes have isolated large areas. The great blizzards of November 1958 in the northwest plains states took 34 lives. Food and fodder were airlifted to the thousands of people and cattle that were marooned by huge snowdrifts and the biting cold. The airlift was called "Operation Haylift."

Dust and sand storms are caused by strong steady winds blowing over loose, dusty, or sandy soil. The sirocco, a foehn wind on the north coast of Africa and Sicily, is the dust and sandstorm wind of the Sahara. The sirocco has many local names: *ghibli* in Libya; *chergui* in Morocco; *chili* in Tunisia; *chichili* in Algeria; and *khamsin* in

Egypt. *Simoom, xaroco, chom, arifi, lampaditsa,* and *sirocco di levante* are a few more of its names.

The *haboob* of the Egyptian Sudan is a dust or sand storm which takes its name from the Arabic word *habb,* which means "wind." This storm, like a wall of sand or dust, often 3,000 feet high, moves across the desert at speeds of 30 to 60 miles an hour. Haboobs can deposit enormous quantities of sand, often burying small villages and caravans trapped out in the desert.

The *karaburan* is the dust storm of the Gobi desert. The *brickfielder* is the name of a hot, dusty north wind which carries dust and sand into Sidney, Australia. Gold miners from Sidney gave the same name to the hot dusty winds of the great central desert of the Aus-

tralian continent. The *harmattan* is the dusty wind that blows south out from the Sahara to the Guinea coast. The harmattan, although hot and dusty, brings such relief from the wet tropical air that it is often called the *doctor.*

Squalls, too, are found all around the world, and are known by many different local names. A *squall* is the name given to a sudden sharp wind, usually accompanied by thunderstorm activity. *Squall lines,* with gusty winds and heavy showers, may extend over hundreds of miles. These lines often form and move across country, well ahead of slowly moving cold fronts, bringing strong winds and drenching rain showers. The gusty strong winds of line squalls and thunder squalls usually blow steadily in one direction. Squalls whose

Steady, strong winds blowing over loose, dry soil become "dust storms." This dust storm, near Springfield, Colorado, was one of many that swept across the plains of the West and Midwest during the drought years of the 1930's.

winds have a rotary motion include *typhoon squalls*, a form of waterspout, which gives first notice of its existence by blowing the sea surface into a froth. The same kind of disturbance, which sailors call the *white squall*, is said to occur with cloudless skies, but meteorologists doubt the existence of such squalls.

Squalls, like foehns, fall winds, and sandstorms, have local names because of their sharp though short-lived effects on local weather. On the Argentine plains the squall is a *pampero;* in the East Indies, a *brubu;* in the Strait of Magellan, a *williwaw;* and on the south coast of Cuba, a *bagamo*. There are probably as many local names for squalls, winds, and other storms all over the world as there are languages.

The map on this page shows winds and windstorms around the world. There are many small areas that also have special winds, but they are too small to show on this map.

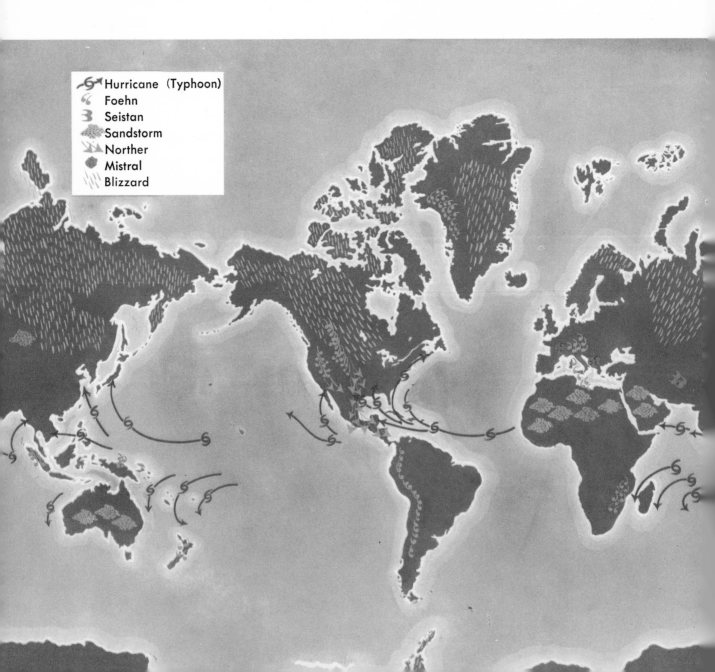

An Indian rain dance in the Southwest.

Weather Lore

Weather affects so many of man's activities that recipes for rainmaking, charms against storms, and incantations to the winds are found in writings throughout history. Scientific efforts to control weather are recent. Meteorologists realize that there is much more to be known about how clouds and raindrops form before weather can be controlled successfully. But our ancestors believed that prayers, charms, and magic rites could coax the weather to behave as they wanted it to behave.

Water brought by the rains is perhaps the most important factor in sustaining life. A man can go without food for weeks if he has water to drink. Without water he would die in a few days. Like men and most animals, plants, which furnish food for all animal life, also die without water. Thus long periods of drought can cause death and starvation, and call for desperate measures to bring rain. So rainmaking was a serious art long before the dawn of written history. Even today, magic ceremonies to charm rain from the skies are performed by certain Indian tribes of the American Southwest, by aborigines of Australia, and by other primitive peoples all over the world.

Many kinds of magic have been used for rainmaking. For each one there is an explanation of why the method should work. These explanations might not seem reasonable today, but they were completely accepted by the people who used the magic.

In India, the frog is supposed to be the favorite of the rain god. The ancient Indians reasoned that if a frog were tied to a stick with its mouth toward the sky, then surely the rain god would send showers to prevent his favorite from dying of thirst. Of course not all of the rain would fall into the frog's mouth, so everyone would benefit from the rain sent to quench the thirst of the frog.

The ancient Hindus and others thought rain would fall if they imitated a rain cloud. A black horse (representing a rain cloud) was rubbed with a black cloth until he neighed, or "thundered." Other imitations of thunderstorms included hitting burning sticks together to throw off sparks in imitation of lightning, thumping tubs, buckets, or drums to produce thunder, and sprinkling water to bring on the rain.

In primitive religions, reptiles, insects, other animals, and idols were associated with rain. Some tribes in the jungles of Central and South America believe that frogs control rain. As insurance these tribes keep a number of frogs penned up in an enclosure, so that when there is a drought, the frogs will be available for whipping. This whipping with a switch is to remind the frogs of their duty to make rain. But too much rain also brings on a whipping.

In parts of Asia, rain gods are persuaded by placing their statues in the blazing sun, so that, in self-defense, they will bring rain to keep cool. Other idols are dragged through dusty fields, beaten, and cursed. Images of the thunder and rain gods are painted upside down on the temple wall. There they remain until

they send rain to wash themselves from their uncomfortable position.

The gods of ancient Greece and Rome were treated with more respect. Zeus, the hurler of thunderbolts, and Jupiter Pluvius, the rainmaker, were offered prayers, wine, food, and fruit in the hope that they would bring rain when needed, and would keep lightning from harming people. Thor and Loki, the ancient Scandinavian gods of thunder and earthquakes, also had offerings made to them by the Norsemen. Thunder was thought to be the noise made

when Thor threw his hammer to the ground. If the hammer hit rocks, the sparks it made when the iron struck stone were the lightning.

Floods were feared just as much as droughts and prayers and magic were used for stopping as well as starting rain. Prayers were offered to gods. Frogs (the most mistreated amphibians) were held under water until at the point of drowning, and idols were left without shelter until the rain stopped.

Wind storms were also hated and feared. The sailors of ancient Greece believed the winds were controlled by the god Aeolus, who played his harp to make gentle breezes, and blew his conch shell trumpet to start the howl-

Man's need for rain has created all sorts of superstitions. In India, the frog was used to appeal to the rain god. The Hindus rubbed a black horse to make rain come. In ancient Greece and Rome, Zeus was appealed to as the god of thunder, and Jupiter Pluvius as the bringer of rain.

Aeolus, the Greek god of winds, blew into a conch shell to start the gales howling.

necessarily follow. The thick, healthy coat of the animal is just the result of a plentiful summer food supply and a healthy appetite. The sound of the cricket, however, can be used, not to predict weather but to find the temperature. If the temperature is neither too hot nor too cold for the cricket, his chirps can be counted and the temperature calculated. Count the number of chirps that can be heard in 15 seconds, then add 32 to get the air temperature in degrees Fahrenheit. In winter, the cricket in the house measures the temperature of the cranny in which he is hiding.

A folk tale says the groundhog can predict weather for six weeks following February 2. Weather experts find no evidence that animals can really forecast weather.

ing gale. One of the aims of these ancient sailors was to find the cave of Aeolus and to trap him within. Then, they thought, he would have to make the winds blow only as they wanted.

There are as many, or more, superstitions and sayings about the weather as there are kinds of weather. Animals, birds, and insects, as well as clouds and winds, were studied to provide clues to coming weather. Many people believe that the groundhog predicts the weather for the six weeks following February 2. If Mr. Groundhog sees his shadow on that date it means only one thing: the sun is shining. If animals have uncommonly thick fur in the autumn, a very cold winter does not

The actions of birds were and still are watched as signs of oncoming weather. The early departure of migratory birds for the south is supposed by many to be a sure sign of an early winter. It is not; it only indicates a food shortage, or an unusually large number

A ring around the moon, caused by cirrus clouds, may indicate coming rain.

of natural enemies, or perhaps that the birds are using last year's calendar.

Of the thousands upon thousands of sayings about weather, a few show that the originators were keen observers of weather. "A ring around the moon brings rain" is valid between 65 and 80 per cent of the time. The ring, or halo, around the moon is seen when there are cirrus clouds overhead. Since cirrus clouds are frequently the fore-runners of a warm front, which brings steady rain, the saying has some truth. But when the cirrus clouds that cause the halo are not associated with a weather situation that brings rain, the old saying fails.

The two sayings about rainbows that follow show a mixture of superstition and truth. *"A Saturday's rainbow, a week's rotten weather"* is a poor pre-diction. A rainbow is seen only when there are raindrops in the air, so the rainbow means only that it is raining where the rainbow is seen. Rain today could be followed by rain tomorrow, but not always, and certainly is not an indication for rain for a week ahead. *"Seven rainbows, eight days of rain"* is perhaps more valid, but only if the seven rainbows are seen on seven suc-cessive days. The eight days of rain would still be a matter of guesswork.

"A veering wind, fair weather;
A backing wind, foul weather."

This couplet is generally true in the Northern Hemisphere, under certain circumstances. For instance, if the wind changes rather rapidly from west to southwest (backing), a cold front with rain is probably moving in rather fast. As the front passes, the wind veers from southwest to west to northwest, and the weather becomes "fair," clearer, and colder.

Many books have been filled with collections of weather sayings and su-perstitions. For each of these books two or three more would be needed to ex-plain why each saying is true, partly true, or completely wrong.

Some day, perhaps, meteorologists will be able to tell exactly why each weather phenomenon occurs, and will be able to forecast the weather exactly, in every detail. But until that day comes, there will always be people who will foretell rain by the actions of the birds, who will warn that stepping on a spider (or ant, or grasshopper) will bring rain, and who will never be at a loss to explain in a detailed, docu-mented, and wholly unscientific way why their forecasts were right or wrong.

Index

Asterisks (*) denote pages on which the subjects are illustrated.

A

PICTURE CREDITS: Harry McNaught, 11, 14, 15, 16, 18, 19, t. 21, 23, 24, b. 26, 29, 30, 35, b. 38, 40, 44, b. 45, 47, 57; Nino Carbe, 6-7, t. 26, 27, 34, 52, 53, 54-55, 56.

Photos: U.S. Department of Commerce, Weather Bureau, p. 10, by Noel M. Klein, 12, 13 Worcester Telegram-Gazette, 21 b., 22, 31, 39, 42, 43; Jerome Wyckoff, 17; Wide World Photos, 20, 33; N. Y. Daily News, 25, 41; courtesy Independent Protection Co., Inc., Goshen, Indiana 28; National Aeronautics and Space Administration, 36, 46, 47; Official U. S. Navy Photo, 37, 45; Rapho-Guillumette, Christian Cambazard, 48.